A Dragon

in Your

Heart

Text and illustrations
by Sophie LeBlanc
with the assistance of
Natacha LeBlanc-Filion

Translation by Peter Frost

Any reproduction, publishing,
printing, or adaptation of this work
by any process whatsoever, be it
electronic or mechanical, in
particular by photocopying or by
microfilming, is prohibited without
written authorization
from the publisher.

ISBN 1 85302 701 4

Jessica Kingsley Publishers
116 Pentonville Road
London N1 9JB, England

e-mail: post@jkp.com
Telephone : 0171-833 2307
Fax : 0171-837 2917

Also available in French
Un dragon dans le cœur

ISBN 2-921912-12-0

Publications MNH Inc.
3947, rue Chabanel
Beauport, Quebec, Canada G1E 4M7
Telephone : (418) 666-8961
© MNH 1999

To Denis and Natacha,
        and also to all families
                going through a similar situation.
                                        S. L.

Laura is coming home from school.
She is running along the sidewalk, twirling her binder around her.
The wind is scattering the leaves in all directions.
The blue-grey sky is shining like metal in the sun.
Suddenly, a large dark cloud blocks out the sun.
It is almost like night out. Laura stops running and feels her heart tighten.

"Oh no," she says. "The monster is coming!"
The cloud passes over. Laura, not fully reassured, continues on her way home.

At home, something unexpected is waiting. Daniel, her father, comes and opens the door.
"Daddy!" she squeals with joy. "You're already back!"
"Please come in," he says tersely.
He seems very concerned. Anne, her mother, is seated in the living room.
She looks like she has been crying. Daniel joins her and motions to Laura to come and sit between them.
"But what's wrong?" asks Laura, starting to worry.
Anne and Daniel exchange glances. Who is going to break the news?

"We've just got back from the doctor's office,"
says Daniel, taking Laura's little hand.
"He said that mommy is sick."

Laura is uneasy. Anne holds her tight against
her own body. "She has cancer," continues Daniel.

"Cancer! Is it serious? I don't want mommy to get
sick! It's not fair!" cries Laura, panic-stricken.

Anne caresses Laura's hair and talks softly.
"Yes, my dear, it's a serious illness.
But the doctor will give me treatments to help me.
I'll be well taken care of, you'll see."
Anne is trying hard to hide her grief but Laura
has already figured out that more
trouble is in store.

In the days that follow, Anne and Daniel
tell everyone the bad news. They talk a lot over the phone.
One after another, friends and relatives make their visit.
Everyone looks stunned. And in all this hubbub, no one is
paying attention to Laura.

"Cancer must be something pretty serious," she says
to herself. "It even makes grown ups afraid!"

Before cancer came into her life, the house
was a happy place to live in. It had a party atmosphere
whenever people came over.
But now everybody looks sad and cross!

Laura is now hearing all kinds of things that adults say
about cancer. They say you can die from it.
They also say the treatments Anne will get are hard
on the body. Laura is afraid. She feels the truth is being
kept from her. "Mommy must be going to die.
That's got to be why no one's saying
anything to me," she tells herself.

One night, unable to go to sleep, Laura hears her mother talking over the phone.
"She's still talking about the cancer," says Laura to herself. "But why doesn't she say anything to me about it?"
This time, Laura has made up her mind. She wants to know. Quietly, she gets out of bed.
She slips out of her bedroom. She stands still, waiting. Finally, after several long minutes her mother
hangs up the phone. Anne is quite surprised to see her Laura standing in the doorway.

"You're still up, my dear? What's wrong? It's well past your bedtime!" says Anne, approaching.
"I know, but I'm afraid mommy!" replies Laura.
Anne smiles, takes Laura by the hand and gently guides her back into the bedroom.

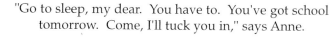

"Go to sleep, my dear. You have to. You've got school tomorrow. Come, I'll tuck you in," says Anne.

But Laura lets go of her mother's hand and draws away. "No, I don't want to go to bed. I want you to tell me what's happening to you."

Surprised, Anne stares at Laura. She sees the troubled face of her little daughter and understands that the time has come to talk. She strokes Laura's head with her hand, trembling a little. "Come my little sweetheart, I'll try to tell you."

She sits down comfortably on the sofa. They snuggle up to each other. Laura anxiously awaits the big explanation. Perhaps she will finally find out what this mysterious cancer is. At last, Anne speaks.

OUR BODY IS MADE OF CELLS.

CANCER HAPPENS WHEN SOME GOOD CELLS
GO CRAZY AND TURN INTO BAD CELLS.

THE CANCER CELLS EAT THE HEALTHY CELLS.

CHEMOTHERAPY ATTACKS ALL OF THE CELLS
THAT REPRODUCE QUICKLY

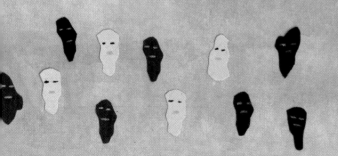

THE CANCER CELLS DIE BUT A LOT OF THE GOOD
CELLS DIE AS WELL.

THE GOOD CELLS COME BACK!
THEY REGENERATE.

"Like I told you, my sickness is called cancer.
As you know, our body is made up of cells.
Cancer happens when some of the good cells go
crazy and turn into bad cells.
These bad cells, the cancer cells, eat the healthy ones.
They reproduce very quickly.
To keep the cancer cells from devouring all of my
good cells, I'll have to get some treatments."

"Yes, but mommy, what do you mean by treatments?
I heard you say they'll be very difficult.
I don't want the treatments to hurt you!" exclaims Laura.

"It's true, Laura. The treatments I'll be getting are very hard on the body.
To destroy the cancer cells, I need a very powerful
medication called chemotherapy.

Chemotherapy especially attacks cells that multiply quickly.
Cancer cells and also some of our healthy cells
may be destroyed by the treatment.
Unfortunately, chemotherapy makes no distinction
between good and bad cells.
It also kills the good ones, so it's
going to make me sick."

"How come? Medication is supposed to make you well, not sick!"
exclaims Laura.

"I know it's not easy to understand. You see, cancer is a very nasty sickness.
So you've got to fight it with all your might.
During the chemotherapy, I'll be sick to my stomach and very tired.
But those effects won't go on forever! The good cells will come back very quickly.
As for the bad ones, well, the chemotherapy may make me sick but those cancer
cells are going to be in for a real thrashing!" explains Anne.

"Really?" says Laura. "And will the bad cells die?"
"Not all at once. But I hope so after several treatments!" answers Anne.
Then she adds, "But I haven't told you everything.
Another effect of the chemotherapy is that I'll lose my hair."

"You'll lose your hair! But why?" says Laura, astonished.
"Because the cells the hair is made up of reproduce very quickly.
They die, so it falls out."

"It'll be gone for good?" says Laura, worriedly.

"Not at all! As soon as the chemotherapy is over, my hair will grow back!"

"Ah, phew!" says Laura, relieved.

"You see, honey, I really hope this treatment will help
me to fight off the cancer. You won't always find the going easy.
I'll be getting very high doses of chemotherapy. At times, I'll be so sick
and tired I'll need to stay a few days at the hospital and ..."

"At the hospital!" Laura cuts in. "I don't want you to go to the hospital!
I'll no longer see you if you go to the hospital! Who'll take care of me?"

"But daddy will still be around! And our friends and family are going
to take turns helping daddy. They'll be on hand for you.
As well, you can always visit me at the hospital.
It won't of course be the same as when I'm at home, but you
won't be all alone, my little darling. I won't be too far away, and
I won't always be at the hospital," answers Anne.

Laura is silent for a moment.
Because she seems very concerned, Anne asks:
"Honey, what's bothering you?" ... No reply.
"Is everything all right my dearest?"
asks Anne a second time.

Laura hesitates, "Er ... yesss, but ...
but I'm not sure you're telling me the truth."

"But of course I'm telling you the truth!" replies Anne, astonished.

"I mean, I'm not sure you've told me the whole truth.
Will you be cured?"

Anne looks at her little daughter gravely.

"Unfortunately, my darling, I can't promise you anything.
All I can tell you is that I'll do my utmost to get cured
and stay with you for a long time."

"But ... but then you might die!"
realizes Laura, raising her voice.

"Yes," finally answers Anne.

That night, Laura lies awake for some time before falling asleep. She now knows that the monster is here.
With its big eye, it watches. It wants to devour her home.
She feels it coming nearer. She hears a murmuring: "Laura ..."
To her great relief she recognizes the voice of her father, who has come to tuck her in.

"Whew! You scared me!" she exclaims.
"Daddy," she adds, snuggling up to him, "Could you please stay with me until I fall asleep?
There's a monster in my room." "O.K. my lovely daughter, but you have to go to sleep, now," replies Daniel.
Once Laura has finally fallen asleep, she has a strange dream.

She is walking in a very dark and sinister forest. It is dark out. The wind is howling in her ears. Laura cries: "Mommy! Mommy! Daddy! Where are you?" She walks ahead as best she can through the branches when finally she glimpses an opening. At the far end of the clearing is a small smoke-filled cottage. In the next instant, she is looking in through the window. She sees a great wizard who is handling several small phials containing funny-looking liquids. He pours the contents into a large cauldron. Ugh! That must be pretty strong stuff! He stirs and stirs! "Voilà," says the wizard. "I think it's ready! You can come now!"

To her great surprise, Laura sees Anne come out of the shadows. She is wearing bright and shining armour with a sun in the middle. The great wizard holds the potion out to Anne. She swallows it and grimaces. Everything turns misty around her. Anne disappears. "Mommy!" cries out Laura.

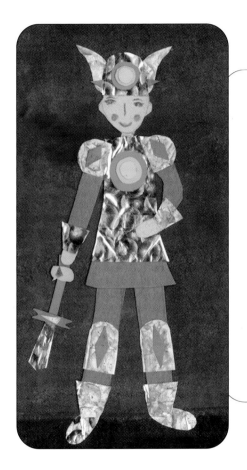

Soon, Anne reappears. She no longer has any hair, but she is smiling. Laura cannot get over just how brave her mother seems!

The wizard brings her a fine golden sword and a helmet to complete the armour.
"Take this," he says solemnly. "You'll need it ..."

Then, suddenly, he turns around and sees Laura at the window.
He smiles, but Laura is very much afraid.
She cries out and wakes up with tears in her eyes.
Fortunately, Daniel is close by.
He consoles Laura who, reassured, goes back to sleep.

Anne has now begun her treatments.
Thanks to the anti-nausea medication, Anne is not too
sick in her stomach. After the chemotherapy treatment, she
quickly becomes very tired and loses her appetite.

Because the chemotherapy has killed her white blood
cells and other cells in her blood, Anne has to
spend a few days at the hospital.

The white blood cells are the soldiers that protect
our bodies against infection.

With no soldiers to defend herself, Anne can
easily catch nasty microbes.
At the hospital, she can be helped out with antibiotics
and blood transfusions to make her stronger.

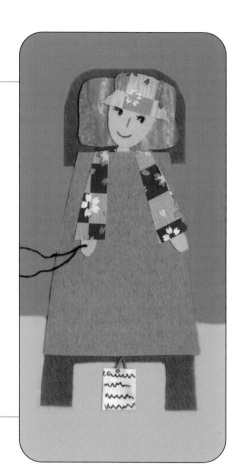

During her hospital stay, Daniel and Laura visit Anne.
Laura crayons pretty drawings every day and writes gentle, sweetly-written letters to her.
She knows that her mother will put them up all over the walls of her room.
The doctors and nurses are all very nice to her. Everybody takes good care of Anne.

Yet Laura does not really enjoy going to the hospital. She is afraid.
Anne has tubes sticking out of her everywhere and is always walking around with
an upright pole from which her medication hangs.
She calls it "Dagwood" to make it more likeable.
Laura knows, however, that her mother does not like it any better!

Laura hates all of these changes that are turning her life upside down. Some days she throws a fit, especially when Daniel wishes to take her to the hospital. Or she may become sullen at mealtime or when she has to do her homework. At such times, Laura feels terribly guilty.

One night, Daniel reproaches Laura for leaving her belongings all over the house and for dragging her feet at homework time.

Laura is very angry. She runs up to her room and locks herself in. She sits on her bed and cries. She cries so hard that it drowns out everything else in the house!

And the monster is there, looking at her with its big eye. "You're not a good girl. You don't listen when you're being asked for something. That's why your mommy is sick," whispers the monster, snickering.

Laura throws a cushion at it. "Go away you wicked monster!" she says. And she weeps harder than ever. Once she has calmed down a bit, the door creaks open halfway.

"May I come in?" asks Daniel.

Laura nods her head. Daniel sits down beside her and puts his arm around her shoulders.

"Is that a bit better? I'm sorry for yelling at you. At times I lose my patience, but sometimes you could also help me out a bit more," he says softly.

"I'm sorry!" says Laura, crying. " I'm not a good girl."

And Laura starts crying even harder. "I'm bad. It's my fault that mommy is sick!"

"Whoever put that idea into your head?" exclaimed Daniel, very surprised. "It's not your fault that mommy is sick!"

Taken aback, Laura looks at Daniel, her round eyes wide open.

21

"It's not my fault?"

"Not one bit! Just imagine what would happen if all the parents in the world got sick every time their children didn't listen! It's normal to get angry, to be in a bad mood, to leave your stuff all over the place, and to not listen sometimes! That sort of thing can make people around us annoyed.
They too can lose their temper.

But that doesn't make them sick! A sickness is never the fault of anyone!"

"But the monster, it's always saying I'm at fault!" replies Laura.
Daniel holds Laura tightly.

"The monster is the one that's no good. You're a very good little girl for me and your mother," he says. Then he adds, "You know, you've got the right to be angry and sad. At times, we too get sad and angry.
It's understandable, you know."

Laura heaves a deep sigh. She is still very sad.
But deep down, she now knows she is not the one who made her mother sick.

Sometimes the monster follows Laura to school. It is always reminding her that her mother is no longer around. When it follows, she can no longer concentrate in class. Her friends are present but she often feels all alone. No one sees the monster, except her! So she stays all by herself and cries. Even though she has good friends, she has the impression that no one understands her. Some children even laugh at her sometimes, because she cries so often. But Laura has a trick up her sleeve. She has an imaginary world. She lives on another planet where there are two suns and three moons.

Lucy, her teacher, often has to bring her back down to earth, but, as soon as she can, she is off and away to new adventures on her planet.

After one treatment, Anne has lost all of her hair! Thankfully she already got it cut very short.
It would have been really sad for her to lose her long locks of hair all at once.
Anne also has a new mania: hats. She has so much fun with her hats that each day
becomes a kind of theatre play that Laura longs to take part in.
Each time, those hats make Anne look like a pretty funny kind of mother!

It is another thing, however, when she goes to pick Laura up
at the school. After the long days of absence, Laura is very happy
to see that her mother can come and pick her up.

At first, she felt deeply embarrassed when the other children
asked Anne: "Do you have any hair left?
Show us what's under your hat!"

Anne always answers the children, and takes her hat off to show them.
The first few times, the other children found her appearance rather strange.
Then, bit by bit, they got used to it.

Now they know that Anne's hair will grow back after the treatments.
They cheer her up and now understand her daughter better.
As for Laura, she no longer feels embarrassed when her mother shows up.

Instead she is very proud to see that her mother still feels
beautiful even without her hair.

Daniel, Anne, and Laura are gradually getting used to their new pace of life.
They have settled down into a new routine. The family now knows how to tell the good days from the bad.
Anne has had several treatments and the cancer is regressing. To put more zest into the home life, Daniel has
given Laura two little chaffinches and some goldfish. Laura likes their daily visit to the pet stores!
Sometimes, they go to the movie theatre and Laura loves the video nights they spend together.

And when the weekend weather is nice, they never miss an opportunity to go for a walk in the park. Sometimes,
to get a breath of fresh air, Daniel and Anne send Laura out to the country to spend a weekend with her cousin.
Laura then takes special care to lock up the monster with two turns of the key before she leaves!

On the good days, Laura may also invite her friends over and go
play with them. She keeps up her activities, including her dance and swim classes.

When mother is home, almost everything returns to normal.
On the good days, friends come over, Laura and her parents
attend family socials, and they go out a little.
Laura really makes the most of those days.
The fun comes back and the monster goes away!
When mother is at the hospital,
things are always a bit sad, but Daniel and Laura have
worked out their own pace of life.

Soon the treatments will be over. Anne has to leave for the hospital once
again and stay there a little while longer. Laura no longer wants her mother to leave.
She is too afraid that Anne will never come back.

Fortunately, Laura's grandmother has come to live in their home for a while.
She takes care of everything. She cooks good wholesome meals, goes out on errands,
brings back little munchies to eat, and goes to pick Laura up at the school every day.
And when the place is in a mess, the monster had better watch out:
Super grandma is around and knows how to clean it up in a jiffy!

Everything seems to be proceeding as with the other cycles of treatment.
Laura goes to see her mother at the hospital with Daniel as often as she can.
Then suddenly, Anne, who used to call every night, no longer phones.
Daniel stops taking Laura to the hospital. He looks worried.
He says Anne is having complications. Daniel even sleeps over at the hospital!
Even grandmother, usually the eternal teaser, has trouble hiding her anxiety.
"That's it," says Laura to herself, "I'll never ever see my mommy again."

And even though everyone tells her that Anne is doing better, even when
Anne herself tells her so, she does not believe.

Grandma is very much aware of the distress her granddaughter is feeling.

One night, she goes to pick Laura up at the school. Her granddaughter is all by her lonesome, grief-stricken with teardrops running down her cheeks. Everywhere in the schoolyard the children joyfully rush up to their mother or father. Grandma draws near to Laura, quietly.

"Poor little thing! You're feeling down? Come here!" says Grandma. Laura, glad to see her grandma come, is welcomed into the wide-open arms.

"What's wrong my little sweetheart? Do you want to tell me?" asks Grandma.

"The others are lucky to have their mommy with them! I may never see my mommy again!" says Laura, holding back a tear.

Grandma, deeply moved, holds her tight and tries to be reassuring.

"But of course you'll see your mommy again! She's already doing much better. You'll see, a few more days and mommy will be back," she says softly.

But that night Laura has a terrible nightmare. She sees a huge horrible four-headed creature with red eyes. It catches her father and mother and Laura cries out, as loud as she can. She hits the huge beast to make it let go of her parents, but it bends over her and opens up the yawning chasm of its gaping mouth. Laura wakes up with a start and cries her eyes out. Grandma gets up and consoles her, until Laura, tuckered out, finally goes back to sleep.

Grandma is wondering what she could do to help her granddaughter get through these bad moments. She thinks back until she remembers what someone had done for her, one day, a long time ago, when she was having nightmares.

That afternoon, on the way home, Grandma tells Laura
one of her childhood memories.

"You know Laura, when I was little, I too would have nightmares
when things weren't going well."

"Really? And what kind of nightmares did you have?
Were you afraid?" asks Laura, interested.

"Oh yes, I was really afraid! There were huge monsters that wanted to eat me,
or nasty thieves who would run after me. It wasn't very funny!
At times, I was so terrorized I no longer wanted to go to sleep!
Then one night my grandfather, who lived with us, came to talk to me.
My grandfather always knew how to find the right words to help us get
over our problems. He was a very wise old man who knew a child's
heart like the back of his hand.

"And what did he tell you?"

"My grandfather believed that the angels watched over us in the world of the invisible. For him,
these angels would help us find the strength to deal with our fears and sorrows. So that night, he came
to talk to me about the angels. He told me I could always speak to them if I was afraid or felt lonely.
Then he took a handkerchief out of his pocket.
And in his handkerchief was a little angel he had carved just for me!
"And did you have other nightmares after that?"
"Hmm ... I think so. But I remember that whenever I was very afraid I would take my little wooden
angel in my hand and I would squeeze it very hard. After, I would feel better and be able to go to sleep."

Laura takes her grandmother's hand. "Me too I'd like to have an angel!" she says.
"Ah, you never know ..." Grandma mysteriously replies.

At home, a surprise is waiting for Laura.
On the table, she finds a beautiful golden box
tied up with a large white ribbon.

"Oh! May I open it Grandma?" asks Laura,
jumping with excitement.

Grandma nods her head. Laura rushes to open up the
box. Once it is open, she sees a beautiful angel
holding a little lamp.

"Oh, thank you Grandma!" says Laura, jumping onto
her and throwing her arms around her neck.
"I hope this little angel will watch over you and help
you keep those nasty nightmares away," says Grandma,
happy to see the stars shine once more in
her granddaughter's eyes.

Laura finds a nice place near her bed for the angel.
The monster does not at all like the new arrival.
Before she leaves her bedroom she looks
at it and makes a face!

After seven long weeks, barely three days before Christmas, Anne is finally released from hospital. Daniel goes to pick her up while Laura and Grandma get the house ready for a small welcome-home party.

When Anne arrives, Laura cannot get over it! She looks so beautiful! Her joy in coming home almost makes everyone forget she has been very sick.

After several weeks of rest at home, with help from Grandma and Daniel, Anne feels much better. Bit by bit, she gets back into her usual activities.

At the start of her convalescence she could not walk to the street corner. Now, she can pick Laura up at the school and make the meals. Laura feels reassured. But when Anne has to go to the hospital for tests or exams, the monster skulks around the house, as if to remind everyone that the cancer could always come back and carry mother away.

Laura is very worried that her mother has gotten sick again.
So much so, that one night the hideous nightmarish creature with four heads comes back.
Only this time, she has no intention of being so easily taken off guard!

A sword suddenly appears.
Laura seizes it and strikes the huge beast.

Then something incredible happens!
The beast turns into a magnificent dragon.
And the dragon says:
"Laura, you've got a lot of courage!

A lot was needed to take on the creature I once was.
You know, within each hideous beast lies a magic dragon like me
who's always willing to help you grow."
"And when I struck down that horrible beast, did that mean my mommy
has been cured forever and ever?" asks Laura, impressed.

"One thing is sure: She's with you now and you have to make the most of every moment you spend with your family. We're all going to die one day. Some will die suddenly, without knowing, like in an accident.

Others will die after a long illness. Sometimes also, you may think you're going to die from an illness and then go on to live a long life. You just never know!" replies the dragon.

"But will you always stay with me and protect me?" she asks.

The dragon breaks into a laugh as loud as a thunderclap.

"But of course, since I'm deep down inside you, in your heart," it replies, softly placing its big paw on Laura's heart.

And so, that morning, Laura wakes up with a dragon in her heart. Looking at the far end of her room, she thinks she glimpses the one-eyed monster. But, after facing a four-headed monster, Laura is much less afraid. With a dragon in your heart, you can get through a lot of obstacles.

A few months later, Grandma gets a surprise in the mail.
It is a letter from Laura!
She rushes to open it up.

"Dear Grandma: We're having loads of fun at the beach.
The doctor said mommy is in remission.
I've included a picture of her with this letter.
Look! Her hair is growing back!"

"See you soon! Hugs and kisses! Yours truly, Laura."

- E n d -

The Cedars Cancer Institute

The Cedars Cancer Institute was established in 1966 by a dedicated group from the Lebanese-Syrian community of Montreal, many of whom remain actively involved today.

Cedars has always attracted talented individuals from different social, economic and ethnic backgrounds, and through their efforts has, over the past 25 years, raised close to six million dollars.

The purpose of the organization was, and continues to be, to raise money in support of hospital cancer words. Early emphasis was placed on research and purchase of state-of-the-art diagnostic and treatment equipment and facilities. Recent efforts have expanded into the areas of cancer education and patient care. A network of psychosocial and humanitarian support for the cancer patients and their families is provided by the Cedars CanSupport program and the recently endowed Wilfrid Howick Humanitarian Fund.

Cedars' strong commitment to cancer education is demonstrated by the creation of the Cedars Cancer Fund Fellowship, providing young cancer specialists with an opportunity to further their education in order to benefit the hospital, the university and, above all, the patient. In addition, Cedars has created two Annual Visiting Professorships in Oncology, which bring world-renowned researchers, educators and physicians to McGill teaching hospitals. The 6-week course in Oncology Nursing given at the hospital provides any nurse with a chance to specialize in the care of cancer patients.

To reflect its ever-growing and expanding commitment, Cedars has recently changed its name from the Cedars Cancer Fund to the Cedars Cancer Institute .

Printed in Canada